Illustrated by Gordon Stowell

Dorcas lived in a busy seaside town called Joppa. In the hot afternoons she sat sewing in the shade by her house.

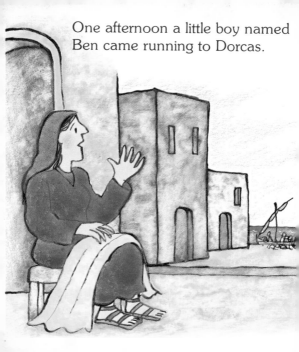

One afternoon a little boy named Ben came running to Dorcas.

"Please come, Dorcas," he cried. "Something's wrong with my mother."

At once Dorcas went to Ben's house. His mother was very sick. "Don't worry," said Dorcas. "I'll help take care of her." And Dorcas stayed to help the sick mother.

Ben's father was dead. His mother had no money to buy clothes.

So when Dorcas went back home,
she made new coats for Ben and
his sister.

Dorcas had many friends. When anyone needed help, they came to her. She enjoyed making clothes for people and telling them about Jesus.

One day Dorcas felt very ill. She had to stay in bed. After a few days she died. Her friends all came to her house. They were so very sad.

Two men came rushing into the house. They said, "Simon Peter is staying in the next town.

He's made a lame man well.
Perhaps he could help Dorcas."

The two men went off to tell Peter about Dorcas. "Please come with us," they said. Quickly Peter went with the two men to the house of Dorcas.

"Peter's coming," someone
shouted.
The women crowded round Peter.

They showed him the clothes Dorcas had made for them and their families.

"Show me the room where Dorcas is," Peter said. He went inside and closed the door. He asked Jesus to make her well. Then he said, "Get up, Dorcas." She opened her eyes and he helped her up.

"Come in now," Peter called to everyone. "Dorcas is well again." All over Joppa people talked about the way Jesus showed His love for Dorcas by helping her to be well again.

You can find the story of Dorcas in the Bible. It is in Acts, chapter 9, verses 36 to 43.

Little Fish Books

Little Fish Books about Bible People
ABRAHAM

Little Fish Books about Bible People
RUTH

Little Fish Books about Bible People
JOHN THE BAPTIST

Little Fish Books about Bible People
PETER